MY DANCE COMPETITION

KEEPSAKE JOURNAL

DATE_____ COMPETITION_____

STUDIO_____ LOCATION_____

DANCE_____

LEVEL

_____

CATEGORY

_____

PLACE
PICTURE
HERE

ADJUDICATION

_____

OVERALL

_____

SPECIALTY AWARD

_____

DATE_____ COMPETITION_____

STUDIO_____ LOCATION_____

DANCE_____

LEVEL

_____

CATEGORY

_____

ADJUDICATION

_____

OVERALL

_____

SPECIALTY AWARD

_____

PLACE
PICTURE
HERE

DATE_____ COMPETITION_____

STUDIO_____ LOCATION_____

DANCE_____

LEVEL

_____

CATEGORY

_____

PLACE
PICTURE
HERE

ADJUDICATION

_____

OVERALL

_____

SPECIALTY AWARD

_____

DATE_____ COMPETITION_____

STUDIO_____ LOCATION_____

DANCE_____

LEVEL

_____

CATEGORY

_____

PLACE
PICTURE
HERE

ADJUDICATION

_____

OVERALL

_____

SPECIALTY AWARD

_____

DATE_____ COMPETITION_____

STUDIO_____ LOCATION_____

DANCE_____

PLACE
PICTURE
HERE

LEVEL

_____

CATEGORY

_____

ADJUDICATION

_____

OVERALL

_____

SPECIALTY AWARD

_____

DATE_____   COMPETITION_____

STUDIO_____   LOCATION_____

DANCE_____

LEVEL

_____

CATEGORY

_____

PLACE
PICTURE
HERE

ADJUDICATION

_____

OVERALL

_____

SPECIALTY AWARD

_____

DATE_____   COMPETITION_____

STUDIO_____   LOCATION_____

DANCE_____

LEVEL

_____

CATEGORY

_____

ADJUDICATION

_____

OVERALL

_____

SPECIALTY AWARD

_____

PLACE
PICTURE
HERE

DATE_____ COMPETITION_____

STUDIO_____ LOCATION_____

DANCE_____

PLACE
PICTURE
HERE

LEVEL

_____

CATEGORY

_____

ADJUDICATION

_____

OVERALL

_____

SPECIALTY AWARD

_____

DATE_____   COMPETITION_____

STUDIO_____   LOCATION_____

DANCE_____

LEVEL

_____

CATEGORY

_____

PLACE
PICTURE
HERE

ADJUDICATION

_____

OVERALL

_____

SPECIALTY AWARD

_____

DATE_____   COMPETITION_____

STUDIO_____   LOCATION_____

DANCE_____

PLACE
PICTURE
HERE

LEVEL

_____

CATEGORY

_____

ADJUDICATION

_____

OVERALL

_____

SPECIALTY AWARD

_____

DATE_____   COMPETITION_____

STUDIO_____   LOCATION_____

DANCE_____

LEVEL

_____

CATEGORY

_____

PLACE
PICTURE
HERE

ADJUDICATION

_____

OVERALL

_____

SPECIALTY AWARD

_____

DATE_____ COMPETITION_____

STUDIO_____ LOCATION_____

DANCE_____

LEVEL

_____

CATEGORY

_____

ADJUDICATION

_____

OVERALL

_____

SPECIALTY AWARD

_____

PLACE
PICTURE
HERE

DATE_____   COMPETITION_____

STUDIO_____   LOCATION_____

DANCE_____

PLACE
PICTURE
HERE

LEVEL

_____

CATEGORY

_____

ADJUDICATION

_____

OVERALL

_____

SPECIALTY AWARD

_____

DATE_____ COMPETITION_____

STUDIO_____ LOCATION_____

DANCE_____

PLACE
PICTURE
HERE

LEVEL

_____

CATEGORY

_____

ADJUDICATION

_____

OVERALL

_____

SPECIALTY AWARD

_____

DATE_____ COMPETITION_____

STUDIO_____ LOCATION_____

DANCE_____

LEVEL

_____

CATEGORY

_____

PLACE
PICTURE
HERE

ADJUDICATION

_____

OVERALL

_____

SPECIALTY AWARD

_____

DATE_____ COMPETITION_____

STUDIO_____ LOCATION_____

DANCE_____

PLACE
PICTURE
HERE

LEVEL

_____

CATEGORY

_____

ADJUDICATION

_____

OVERALL

_____

SPECIALTY AWARD

_____

DATE_____ COMPETITION_____

STUDIO_____ LOCATION_____

DANCE_____

PLACE
PICTURE
HERE

LEVEL

_____

CATEGORY

_____

ADJUDICATION

_____

OVERALL

_____

SPECIALTY AWARD

_____

DATE_____ COMPETITION_____

STUDIO_____ LOCATION_____

DANCE_____

PLACE
PICTURE
HERE

LEVEL

_____

CATEGORY

_____

ADJUDICATION

_____

OVERALL

_____

SPECIALTY AWARD

_____

DATE_____   COMPETITION_____

STUDIO_____   LOCATION_____

DANCE_____

LEVEL

_____

CATEGORY

_____

PLACE
PICTURE
HERE

ADJUDICATION

_____

OVERALL

_____

SPECIALTY AWARD

_____

DATE_____ COMPETITION_____

STUDIO_____ LOCATION_____

DANCE_____

PLACE
PICTURE
HERE

LEVEL

_____

CATEGORY

_____

ADJUDICATION

_____

OVERALL

_____

SPECIALTY AWARD

_____

DATE_____   COMPETITION_____

STUDIO_____   LOCATION_____

DANCE_____

PLACE
PICTURE
HERE

LEVEL

_____

CATEGORY

_____

ADJUDICATION

_____

OVERALL

_____

SPECIALTY AWARD

_____

DATE_____ COMPETITION_____

STUDIO_____ LOCATION_____

DANCE_____

PLACE
PICTURE
HERE

LEVEL

_____

CATEGORY

_____

ADJUDICATION

_____

OVERALL

_____

SPECIALTY AWARD

_____

DATE_____   COMPETITION_____

STUDIO_____   LOCATION_____

DANCE_____

LEVEL

_____

CATEGORY

_____

ADJUDICATION

_____

OVERALL

_____

SPECIALTY AWARD

_____

PLACE
PICTURE
HERE

DATE_____ COMPETITION_____

STUDIO_____ LOCATION_____

DANCE_____

PLACE
PICTURE
HERE

LEVEL

_____

CATEGORY

_____

ADJUDICATION

_____

OVERALL

_____

SPECIALTY AWARD

_____

DATE_____ COMPETITION_____

STUDIO_____ LOCATION_____

DANCE_____

LEVEL

_____

CATEGORY

_____

PLACE
PICTURE
HERE

ADJUDICATION

_____

OVERALL

_____

SPECIALTY AWARD

_____

DATE_____   COMPETITION_____

STUDIO_____   LOCATION_____

DANCE_____

LEVEL

_____

CATEGORY

_____

PLACE
PICTURE
HERE

ADJUDICATION

_____

OVERALL

_____

SPECIALTY AWARD

_____

DATE_____ COMPETITION_____

STUDIO_____ LOCATION_____

DANCE_____

LEVEL

_____

CATEGORY

_____

PLACE
PICTURE
HERE

ADJUDICATION

_____

OVERALL

_____

SPECIALTY AWARD

_____

DATE_____   COMPETITION_____

STUDIO_____   LOCATION_____

DANCE_____

LEVEL

_____

CATEGORY

_____

ADJUDICATION

_____

OVERALL

_____

SPECIALTY AWARD

_____

PLACE
PICTURE
HERE

DATE_____ COMPETITION_____

STUDIO_____ LOCATION_____

DANCE_____

PLACE
PICTURE
HERE

LEVEL

_____

CATEGORY

_____

ADJUDICATION

_____

OVERALL

_____

SPECIALTY AWARD

_____

DATE_____   COMPETITION_____

STUDIO_____   LOCATION_____

DANCE_____

LEVEL

_____

CATEGORY

_____

ADJUDICATION

_____

OVERALL

_____

SPECIALTY AWARD

_____

PLACE
PICTURE
HERE

DATE_____ COMPETITION_____

STUDIO_____ LOCATION_____

DANCE_____

PLACE
PICTURE
HERE

LEVEL

_____

CATEGORY

_____

ADJUDICATION

_____

OVERALL

_____

SPECIALTY AWARD

_____

DATE_____   COMPETITION_____

STUDIO_____   LOCATION_____

DANCE_____

LEVEL

_____

CATEGORY

_____

ADJUDICATION

_____

OVERALL

_____

SPECIALTY AWARD

_____

PLACE
PICTURE
HERE

DATE_____ COMPETITION_____

STUDIO_____ LOCATION_____

DANCE_____

LEVEL

_____

CATEGORY

_____

PLACE
PICTURE
HERE

ADJUDICATION

_____

OVERALL

_____

SPECIALTY AWARD

_____

DATE_____   COMPETITION_____

STUDIO_____   LOCATION_____

DANCE_____

LEVEL

_____

CATEGORY

_____

PLACE
PICTURE
HERE

ADJUDICATION

_____

OVERALL

_____

SPECIALTY AWARD

_____

DATE_____   COMPETITION_____

STUDIO_____   LOCATION_____

DANCE_____

PLACE
PICTURE
HERE

LEVEL

_____

CATEGORY

_____

ADJUDICATION

_____

OVERALL

_____

SPECIALTY AWARD

_____

DATE_____ COMPETITION_____

STUDIO_____ LOCATION_____

DANCE_____

PLACE
PICTURE
HERE

LEVEL

_____

CATEGORY

_____

ADJUDICATION

_____

OVERALL

_____

SPECIALTY AWARD

_____

DATE_____ COMPETITION_____

STUDIO_____ LOCATION_____

DANCE_____

LEVEL

_____

CATEGORY

_____

PLACE
PICTURE
HERE

ADJUDICATION

_____

OVERALL

_____

SPECIALTY AWARD

_____

DATE_____ COMPETITION_____

STUDIO_____ LOCATION_____

DANCE_____

LEVEL

_____

CATEGORY

_____

PLACE
PICTURE
HERE

ADJUDICATION

_____

OVERALL

_____

SPECIALTY AWARD

_____

DATE_____ COMPETITION_____

STUDIO_____ LOCATION_____

DANCE_____

PLACE
PICTURE
HERE

LEVEL

_____

CATEGORY

_____

ADJUDICATION

_____

OVERALL

_____

SPECIALTY AWARD

_____

DATE_____ COMPETITION_____

STUDIO_____ LOCATION_____

DANCE_____

PLACE
PICTURE
HERE

LEVEL

_____

CATEGORY

_____

ADJUDICATION

_____

OVERALL

_____

SPECIALTY AWARD

_____

DATE_____   COMPETITION_____

STUDIO_____   LOCATION_____

DANCE_____

LEVEL

_____

CATEGORY

_____

PLACE
PICTURE
HERE

ADJUDICATION

_____

OVERALL

_____

SPECIALTY AWARD

_____

DATE_____ COMPETITION_____

STUDIO_____ LOCATION_____

DANCE_____

LEVEL

_____

CATEGORY

_____

ADJUDICATION

_____

OVERALL

_____

SPECIALTY AWARD

_____

PLACE
PICTURE
HERE

DATE_____ COMPETITION_____

STUDIO_____ LOCATION_____

DANCE_____

PLACE
PICTURE
HERE

LEVEL

_____

CATEGORY

_____

ADJUDICATION

_____

OVERALL

_____

SPECIALTY AWARD

_____

DATE_____ COMPETITION_____

STUDIO_____ LOCATION_____

DANCE_____

PLACE
PICTURE
HERE

LEVEL

_____

CATEGORY

_____

ADJUDICATION

_____

OVERALL

_____

SPECIALTY AWARD

_____

DATE_____   COMPETITION_____

STUDIO_____   LOCATION_____

DANCE_____

LEVEL

_____

CATEGORY

_____

ADJUDICATION

_____

OVERALL

_____

SPECIALTY AWARD

_____

PLACE
PICTURE
HERE

DATE_____   COMPETITION_____

STUDIO_____   LOCATION_____

DANCE_____

PLACE
PICTURE
HERE

LEVEL

_____

CATEGORY

_____

ADJUDICATION

_____

OVERALL

_____

SPECIALTY AWARD

_____

DATE_____   COMPETITION_____

STUDIO_____   LOCATION_____

DANCE_____

LEVEL

_____

CATEGORY

_____

ADJUDICATION

_____

OVERALL

_____

SPECIALTY AWARD

_____

PLACE
PICTURE
HERE

DATE_____   COMPETITION_____

STUDIO_____   LOCATION_____

DANCE_____

PLACE
PICTURE
HERE

LEVEL

_____

CATEGORY

_____

ADJUDICATION

_____

OVERALL

_____

SPECIALTY AWARD

_____

DATE_____   COMPETITION_____

STUDIO_____   LOCATION_____

DANCE_____

LEVEL

_____

CATEGORY

_____

ADJUDICATION

_____

OVERALL

_____

SPECIALTY AWARD

_____

PLACE
PICTURE
HERE

CREATED WITH ♥ BY MELANIE SALAS
A MOM OF 2 DAUGHTERS AND FORMER ELEMENTARY TEACHER

My Dance Competition Keepsake Journal Created by Melanie Salas
Published by Golden Crown Publishing, LLC

www.GoldenCrownPublishing.com

© 2021 Golden Crown Publishing, LLC

Created by Melanie Salas

'

ISBN:978-1-954648-30-2

Made in the USA
Las Vegas, NV
29 November 2023

81654462R00057